ANIMAL
MAZES

45 Wild Mazes Packed with Nature Facts →

Art by Marc Pattenden
Words by Laura Baker

ARCTURUS

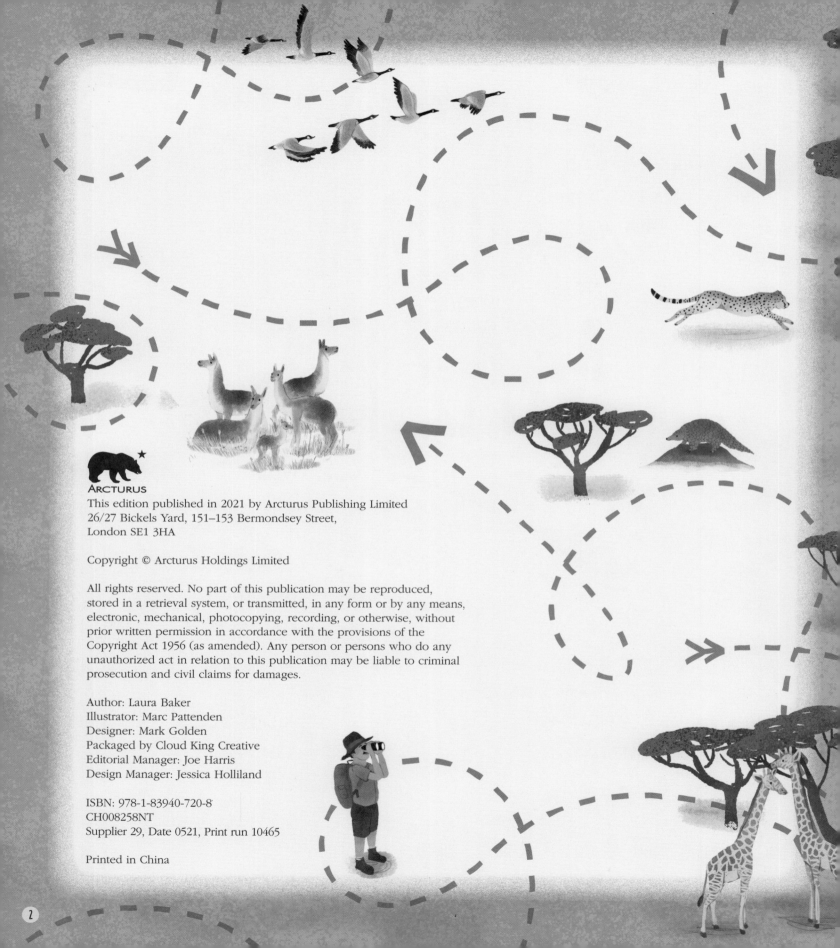

ARCTURUS

This edition published in 2021 by Arcturus Publishing Limited
26/27 Bickels Yard, 151–153 Bermondsey Street,
London SE1 3HA

Author: Laura Baker
Illustrator: Marc Pattenden
Designer: Mark Golden
Packaged by Cloud King Creative
Editorial Manager: Joe Harris
Design Manager: Jessica Holliland

ISBN: 978-1-83940-720-8
CH008258NT
Supplier 29, Date 0521, Print run 10465

Printed in China

CONTENTS

IN THE ICY ARCTIC

At the top of the world, animals have adapted to roam and survive on snow and ice. Welcome to the Arctic!

SHOW THIS EXPLORER THE WAY THROUGH THE SNOWY DRIFTS TO THE WARM RESEARCH BASE.

START

Under their thick, transparent fur coat, polar bears have black skin that soaks up the sun to help keep them warm.

The Arctic hare changes its fur to match its surroundings—from brown like the rocks in summer to white like snow in winter.

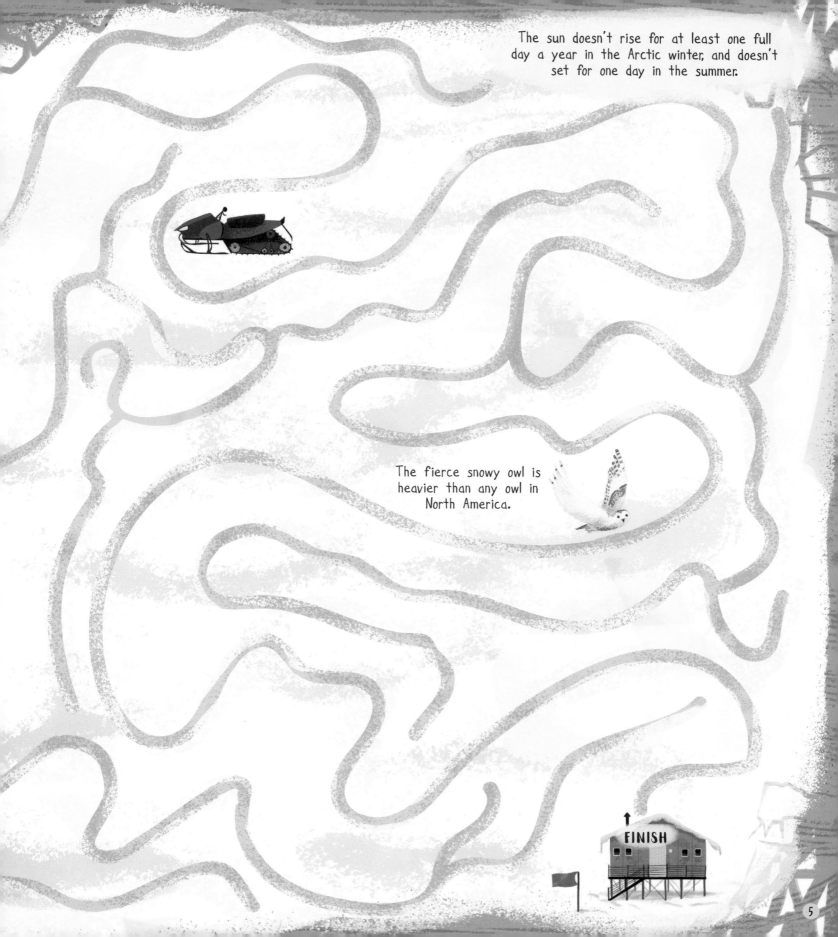

The sun doesn't rise for at least one full day a year in the Arctic winter, and doesn't set for one day in the summer.

The fierce snowy owl is heavier than any owl in North America.

FINISH

CREATURES OF THE COLD

The Arctic Ocean may be the world's smallest ocean, but it is home to many fascinating creatures, both above and below the ice.

START

CAN YOU LEAD THE BOAT THROUGH THE ICY WATERS?

The narwhal is often called the unicorn of the sea. Its horn is actually a tooth that can grow up to 3 m (10 feet) long—longer than the tallest person on Earth!

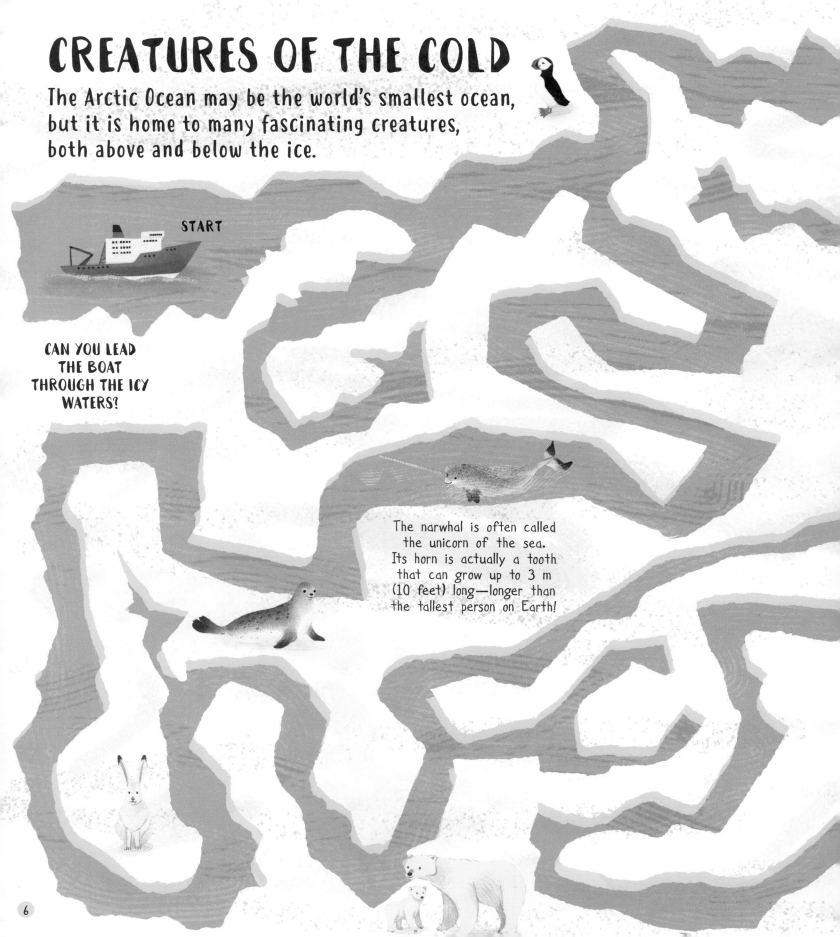

Walruses hook their tusks on to ice to help them climb out of icy waters.

The beluga whale is the only whale with white skin, perfect for camouflage amongst polar ice caps.

FINISH

ROAMING IN THE ROCKIES

High in the Rocky Mountains, animals big and small climb craggy cliffs and roam rocky terrain. Watch your step!

The dangling flap of skin that hangs from a moose's neck is called a bell.

The small collared pika lets out a shrill, short alarm call when it spots predators.

START

HELP THE EXPLORERS REACH THE TOP OF THE MOUNTAIN.

The Rocky Mountains stretch all the way from northwestern Canada down through the United States.

Listen for the sound of clashing horns—that's male bighorn sheep headbutting each other over and over, fighting for the top spot.

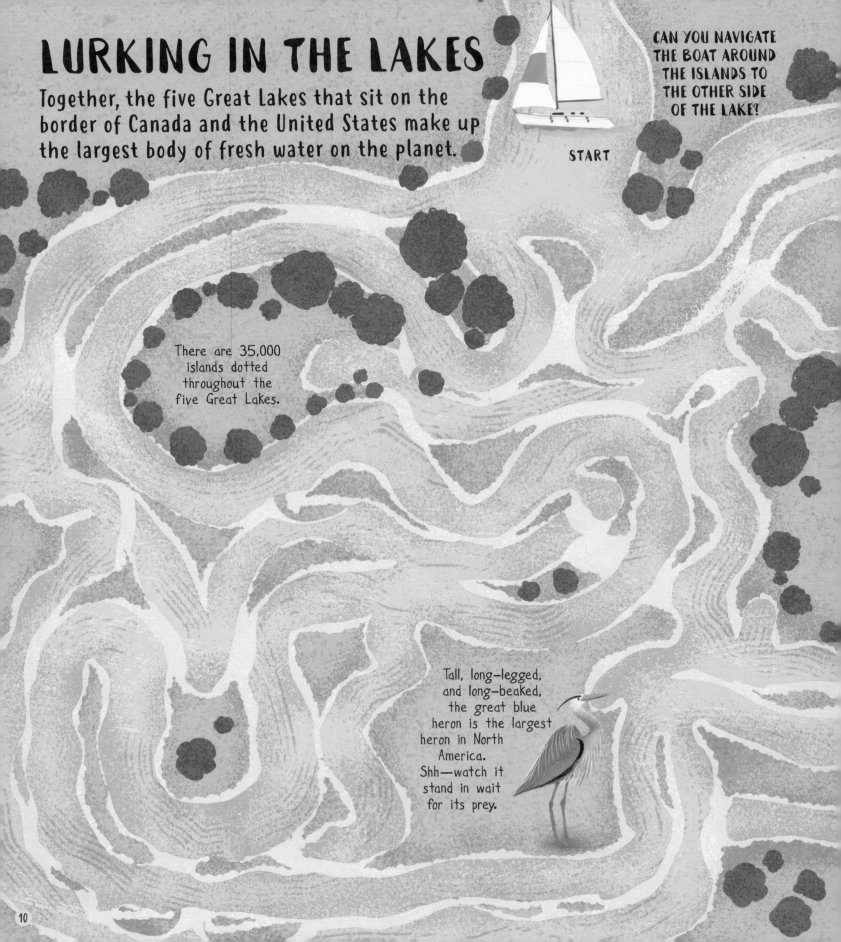

LURKING IN THE LAKES

Together, the five Great Lakes that sit on the border of Canada and the United States make up the largest body of fresh water on the planet.

CAN YOU NAVIGATE THE BOAT AROUND THE ISLANDS TO THE OTHER SIDE OF THE LAKE?

START

There are 35,000 islands dotted throughout the five Great Lakes.

Tall, long-legged, and long-beaked, the great blue heron is the largest heron in North America. Shh—watch it stand in wait for its prey.

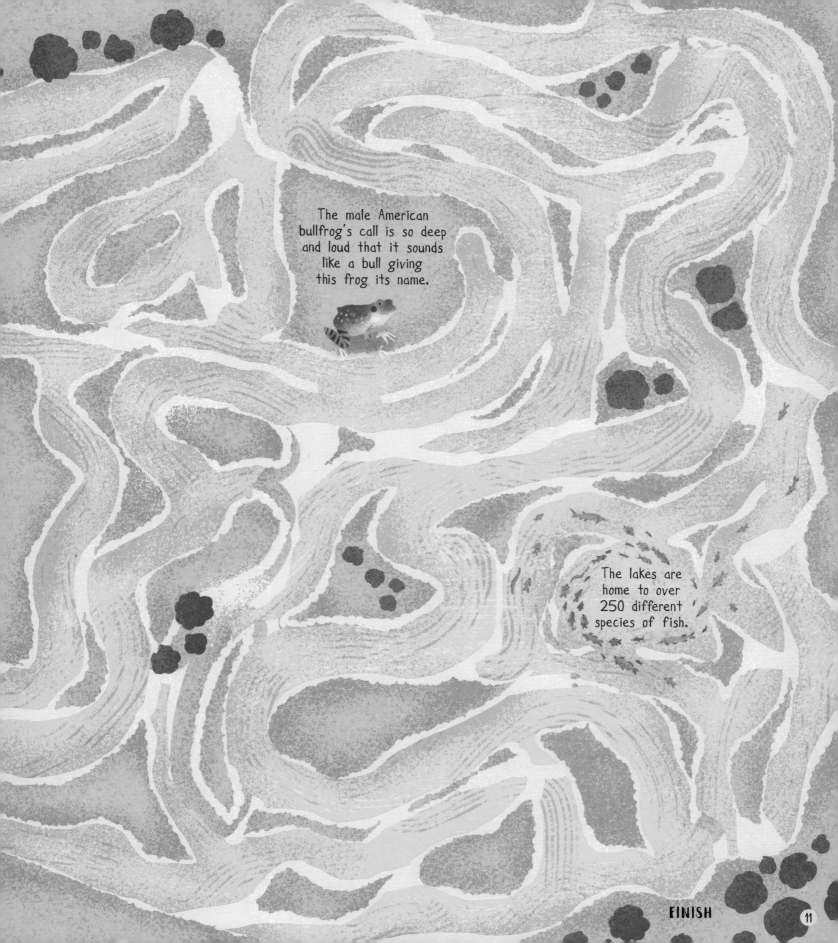

The male American bullfrog's call is so deep and loud that it sounds like a bull giving this frog its name.

The lakes are home to over 250 different species of fish.

FINISH

WOODLAND WILDERNESS

Amongst evergreens and leafy trees, tough and smart animals call the forests of Canada home.

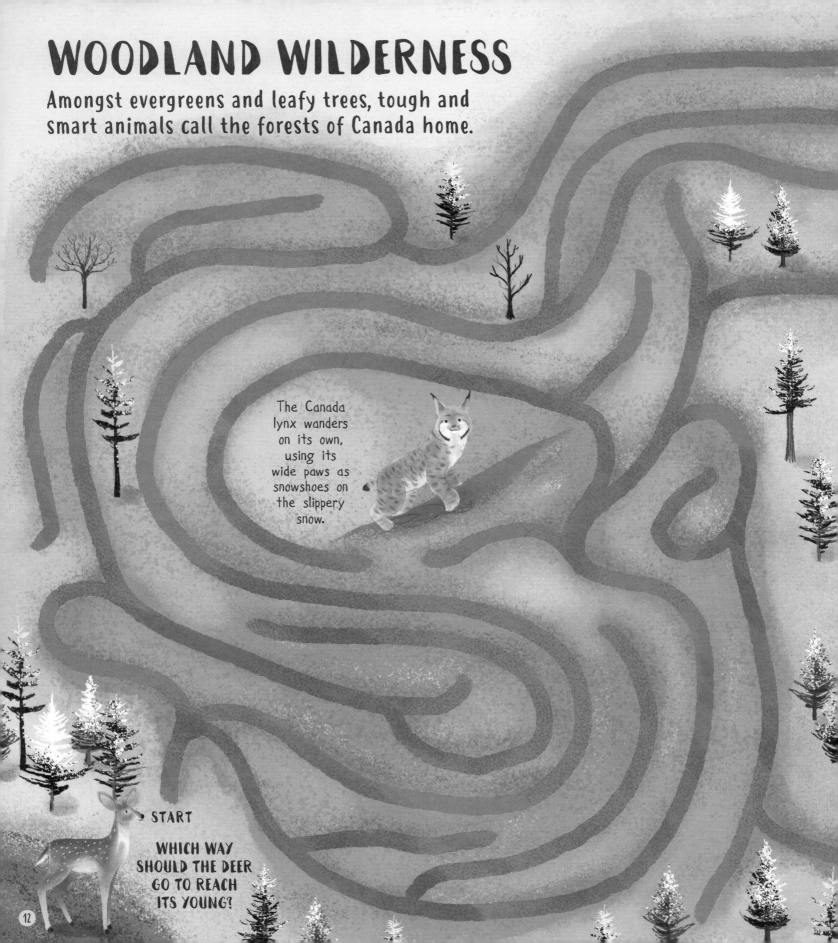

The Canada lynx wanders on its own, using its wide paws as snowshoes on the slippery snow.

START

WHICH WAY SHOULD THE DEER GO TO REACH ITS YOUNG?

A porcupine's quills are in fact sharp hairs. There can be 30,000 quills on just one porcupine!

Stealthy wolves use their voice, body language, and even scent to communicate with others in the pack.

IN THE SKIES

Turn your gaze upward as you
walk through the trees.
Who can you see
soaring above?

Canada geese can travel far and fast to find
warmer weather. They have been known to cross
2,400 km (1,500 mi) in just 24 hours.

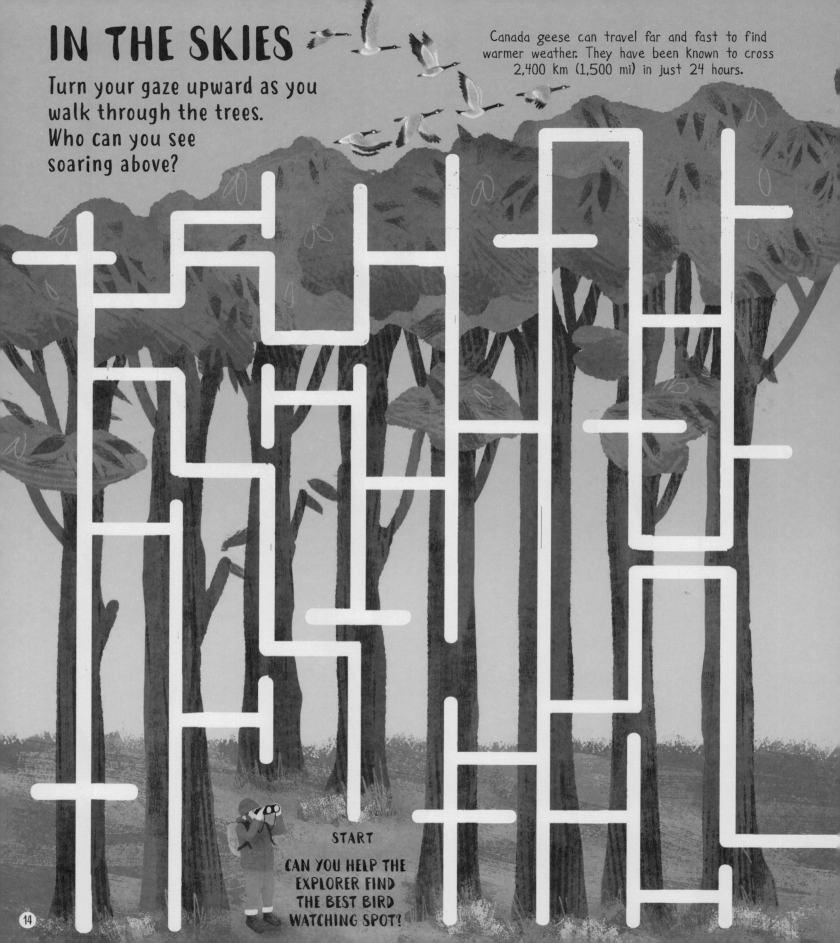

START

CAN YOU HELP THE
EXPLORER FIND
THE BEST BIRD
WATCHING SPOT?

FINISH

Woodpeckers peck
their beaks against
tree trunks as fast
as 20 times
per second.

Is it a bird?
Is it a plane?
No, it's a flying squirrel,
using the webbing between
its wrists and ankles to
glide and soar away from
predators below.

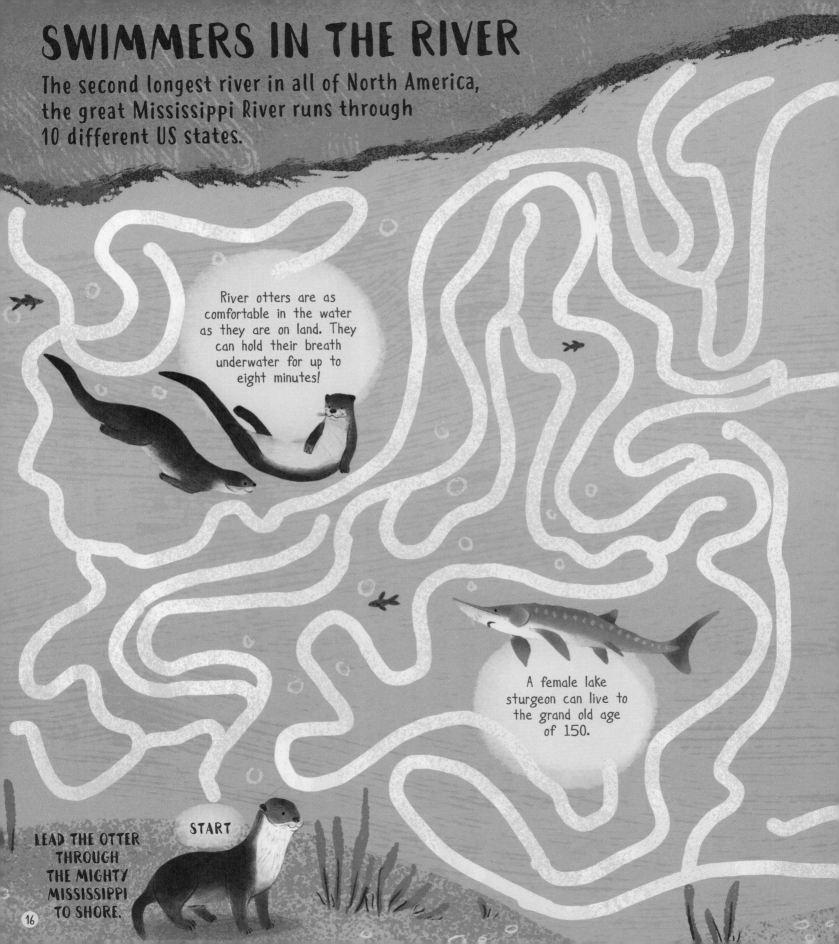

SWIMMERS IN THE RIVER

The second longest river in all of North America, the great Mississippi River runs through 10 different US states.

River otters are as comfortable in the water as they are on land. They can hold their breath underwater for up to eight minutes!

A female lake sturgeon can live to the grand old age of 150.

START

LEAD THE OTTER THROUGH THE MIGHTY MISSISSIPPI TO SHORE.

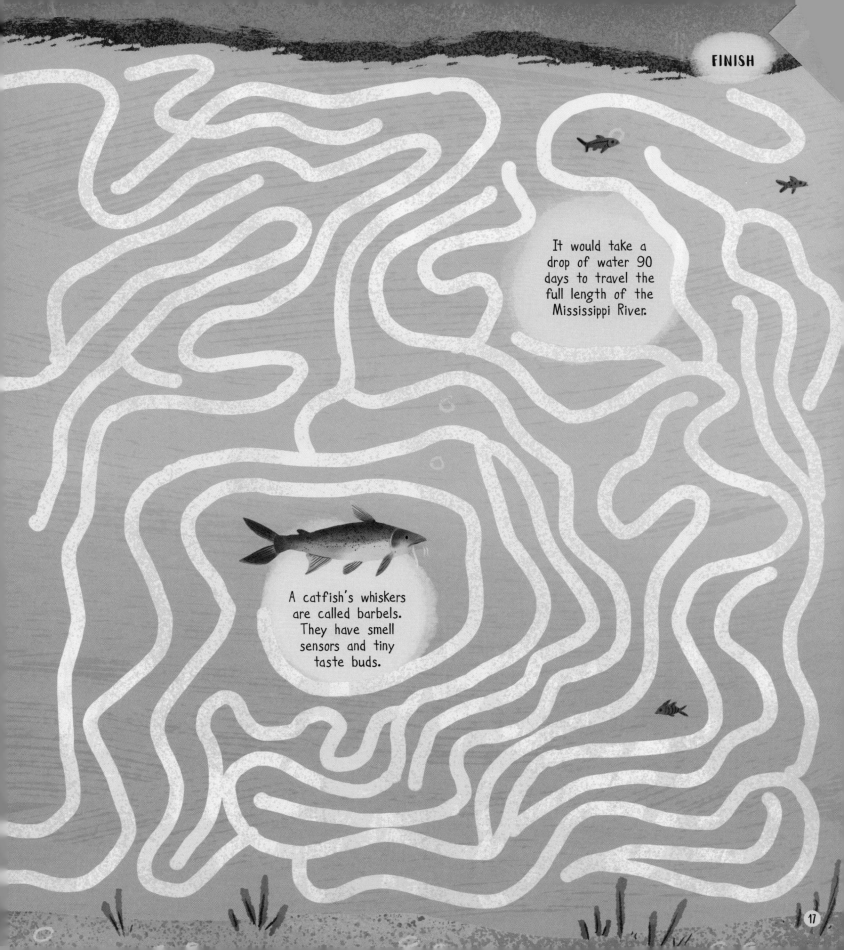

FINISH

It would take a drop of water 90 days to travel the full length of the Mississippi River.

A catfish's whiskers are called barbels. They have smell sensors and tiny taste buds.

ON THE BANKS

Along the water's edge, riverbanks host many dens, lodges, and homes for a variety of busy animals.

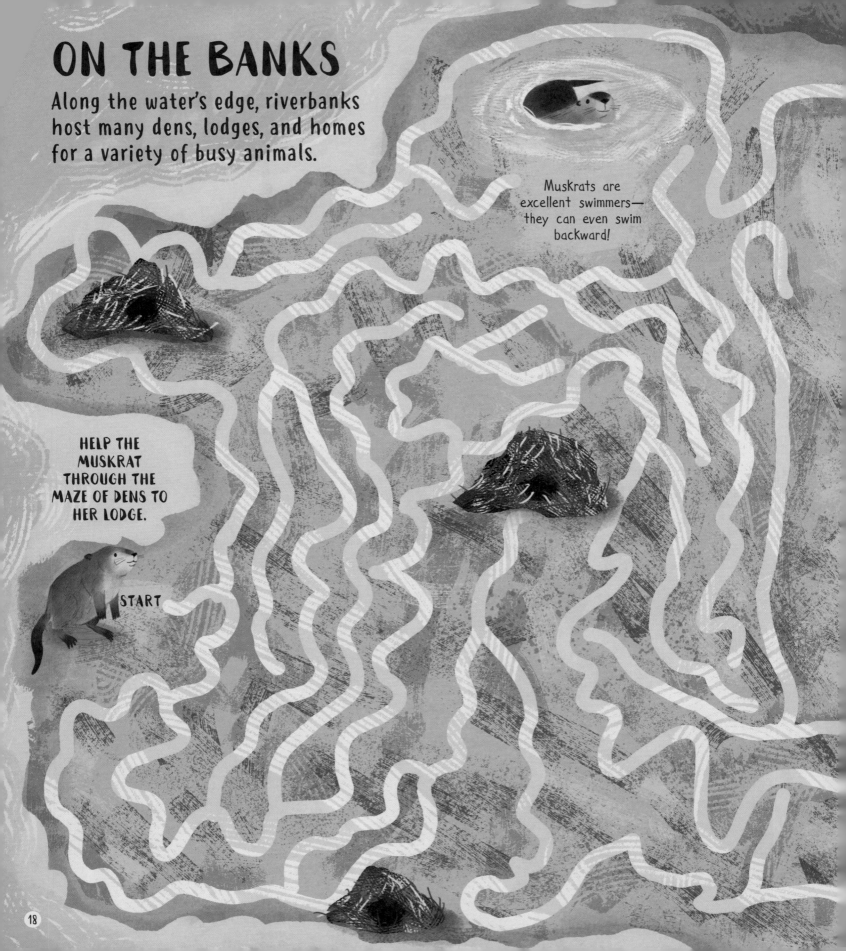

Muskrats are excellent swimmers— they can even swim backward!

HELP THE MUSKRAT THROUGH THE MAZE OF DENS TO HER LODGE.

START

FINISH

Beavers' teeth never stop growing! Their teeth are so strong that they can bite down entire trees.

Coyotes creep around many habitats, including along riverbanks. They are fast runners and powerful swimmers.

ABOVE THE RIVER

While the river flows below, birds soar above, using the water and its banks for food and shelter.

CAN YOU SHOW THE BALD EAGLE THE WAY THROUGH THE TREES TO ITS NEST?

START

Kingfishers make their nests not in trees, but in burrows on the riverbank.

Coots like to make floating nests among plants in the water.

20

Many birds use the Mississippi River as a path to follow when they fly south for the winter, and when they return north again!

FINISH

Bald eagles' huge nests are called aeries. They are usually built high up in trees to keep eggs safe.

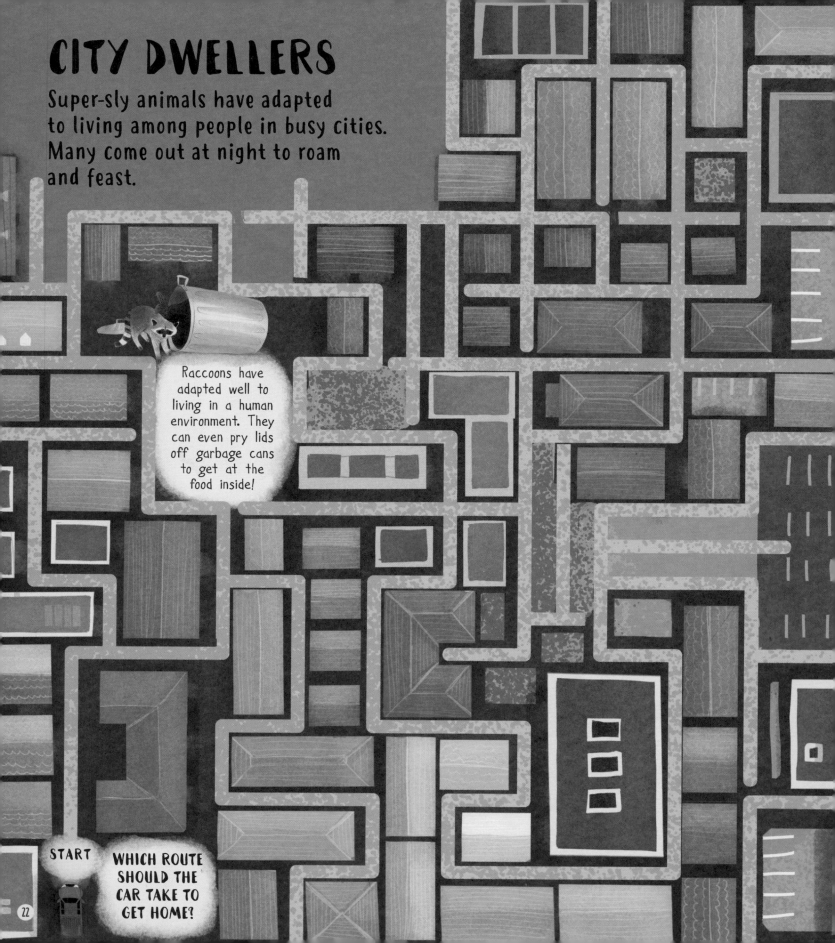

Urban foxes can sometimes be found in dens under porches or sheds.

Once little kits are ready to go out in the world, they move on from their den.

FINISH

A skunk's spray can reach up to 3.7 m (12 ft) away—so stand far back if you see them stomp their feet and lift their tail!

IN THE YARD

Close to home, animals play and prey.
Some are wild and some are tame.

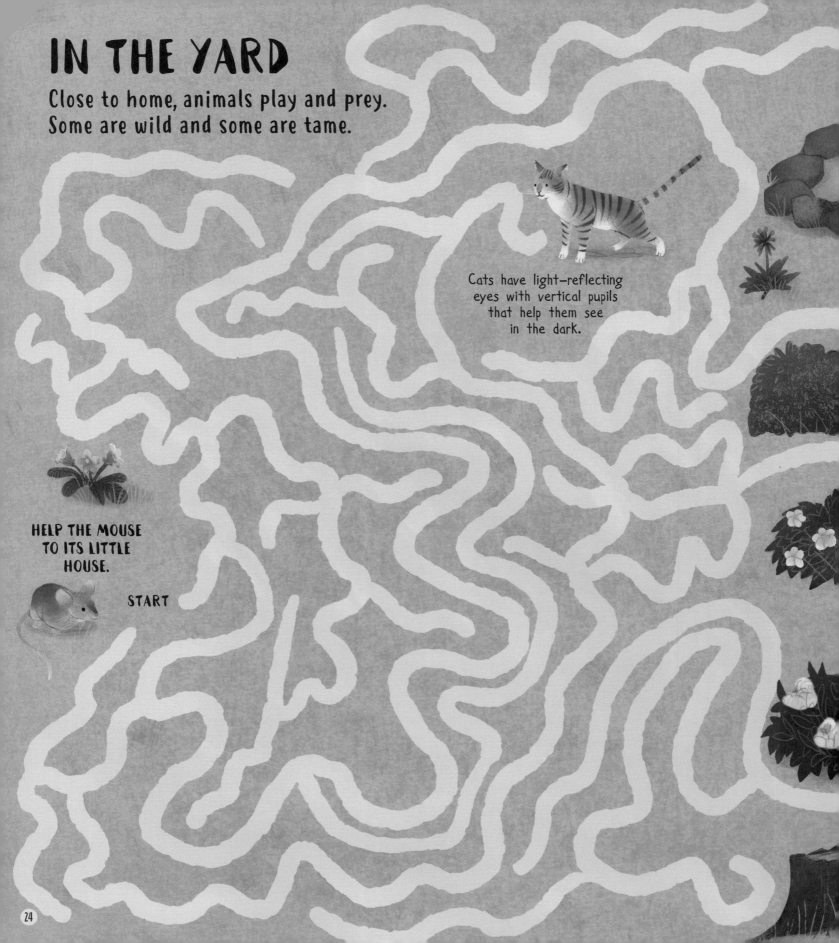

Cats have light-reflecting
eyes with vertical pupils
that help them see
in the dark.

**HELP THE MOUSE
TO ITS LITTLE
HOUSE.**

START

In just two days, chipmunks can gather all the food they need to last an entire winter!

FINISH

Dogs were probably the first animal to be tamed by humans, many thousands of years ago.

BUG HOTEL

One small bug shelter can be teeming with tiny critters, working their way through tunnels and curling up in comfy bark beds.

Snails have just one foot! It ripples to move the snail along on a path of slippery mucus.

Caterpillars have tiny hooks on their feet to help them climb plants.

LEAD THE CATERPILLAR THROUGH THE GAPS TO THE LEAVES.

START

Woodlice shed their shells in an unusual way as they grow—first the back half falls off, and then the front half follows a few days later.

FINISH

There are over 45,000 species of spider across the world.
All produce silk, but only some use it for their webs—others
use it to climb, wrap up prey, or make nests.

PADDLING IN THE POND

Watch wondrous wildlife flit, dip, and swim in small but thriving ponds.

START

SHOW THE FROG THE WAY ACROSS THE LILY PADS TO SHORE AVOIDING THE FLOWERS.

Pond skaters, or water striders, have tiny water-repellent hairs on the bottom of their feet that help them walk on water.

Frogs can breathe through their skin as well as their lungs.

Ancestors of dragonflies lived 325 million years ago— making them older than dinosaurs!

FINISH

AT HOME IN HONEYCOMB

In the wild, honeybees live in hives full of honeycomb, where their young are housed and food is stored.

Up to 50,000 bees can live in a single hive!

In the winter, honeybees huddle into a ball to keep warm.

START

CAN YOU HELP THE WORKER BEE TAKE HER FOOD TO THE QUEEN?

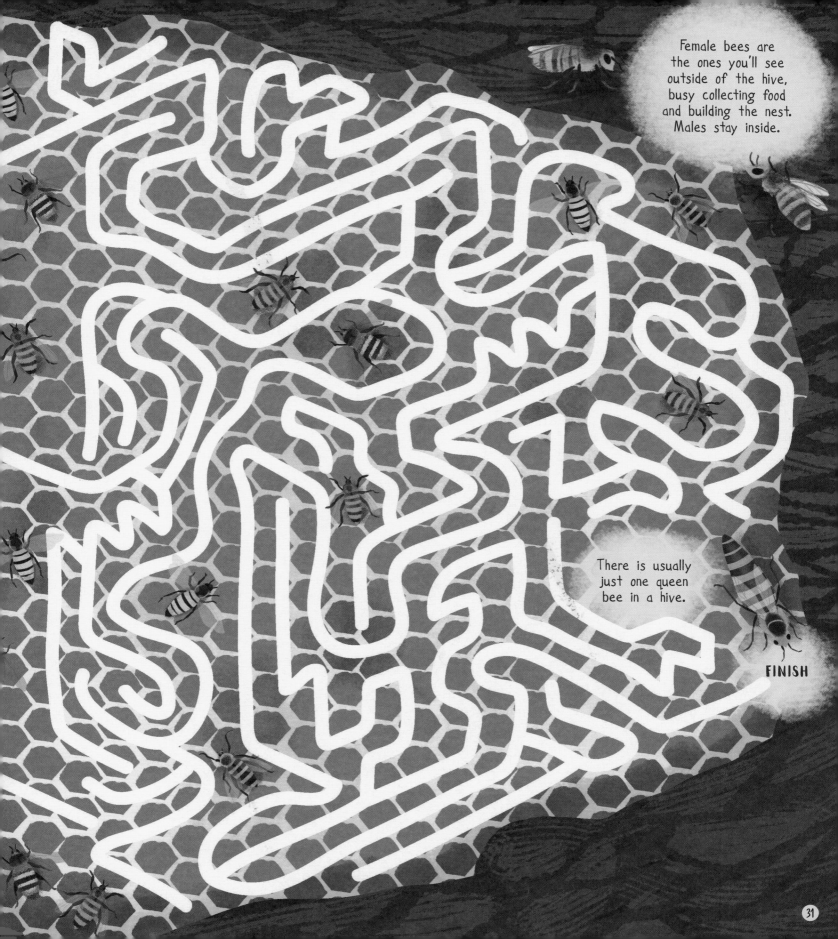

Female bees are the ones you'll see outside of the hive, busy collecting food and building the nest. Males stay inside.

There is usually just one queen bee in a hive.

FINISH

PROWLING ON THE PRAIRIES

Look closely at the vast Great Plains. Amongst the sweeping wilderness, animals build, burrow, and wander.

The pronghorn is the fastest land animal in North America. It can run at speeds of 96 km/h (60 mph)—nearly as fast as a car on a freeway!

The rare black-footed ferret uses its long, thin body to creep into the burrows of its prey—mainly the prairie dog.

START

GUIDE THE EXPLORERS ACROSS THE PRAIRIE TO TOWN.

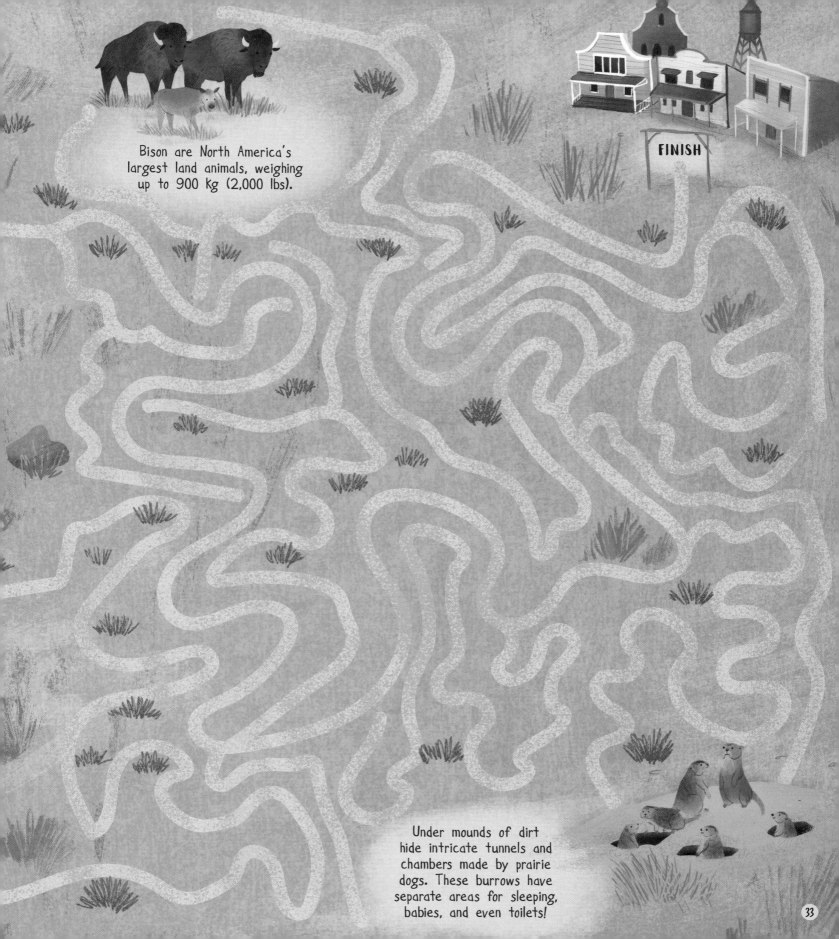

Bison are North America's largest land animals, weighing up to 900 kg (2,000 lbs).

FINISH

Under mounds of dirt hide intricate tunnels and chambers made by prairie dogs. These burrows have separate areas for sleeping, babies, and even toilets!

IN THE GRASSLANDS

Grasslands cover about 13% of South America, in areas called paramos, punas, pampas, campos, and the Patagonian steppe.

HELP THE GREATER RHEA RUN THROUGH THE PAMPAS TO HER NEST.

START

The greater rhea is the largest bird in South America—but it cannot fly.

A baby guanaco is called a chulengo. It can walk from the moment it is born.

UP IN THE ANDES

In the world's longest mountain range, you can find high peaks, rumbling volcanoes, and rugged creatures.

The massive Andean condor has a completely bald head.

START

CAN YOU SHOW THE EXPLORERS THE WAY TO REACH THE SUMMIT?

Chinchillas have thick fur to keep them warm. But if they get too hot, they can use their large ears to let out heat!

Llamas are relatives of camels—without the hump. Their flat backs make them perfect pack animals for people of the Andes.

The smallest of the camel family, the vicuña has remained wild and undomesticated. It is known for its long, fine, silky yet strong coat.

BIRDS OF THE AMAZON

When you step into the bright and tropical Amazon rain forest, be sure to look up! The dense canopy of trees is home to over 1,300 diverse species of beautiful birds.

The Amazon parrot is a master at listening to and repeating sounds. Some can even mimic human speech.

CAN YOU HELP THE EXPLORER FIND HIS WAY THROUGH THE RAIN FOREST TO HIS HUT?

START

The toco toucan's long, bright bill is a third of its whole body length!

The Amazon rain forest covers 5.5 million km² (2.1 million square mi) of our planet—that's nearly twice the size of India!

The noisy scarlet macaw fills the forest with its squawks and screeches, used to communicate with others of its kind.

FINISH

BELOW THE CANOPY

Between the canopy of trees and the rain forest floor, hundreds of animals and reptiles hunt, sleep, and creep.

HELP THE TAPIR GET SAFELY THROUGH THE FOREST.

START

Slithering through swamps and streams, the green anaconda is the largest snake in the world. It can weigh up to 225 kg (500 lbs)— half as much as a horse.

The golden poison frog is only the size of a paperclip, but it has enough poison in its skin to kill 10 adults.

In the trees, time stands still with the world's slowest mammal. A sloth moves so gradually that algae grows on its fur.

The jaguar is the third biggest cat in the world, but it has the most powerful bite of them all.

FINISH

41

IN THE TROPICS

If you sail way out to the middle of the Pacific Ocean, you'll find a group of islands with their own unique sea and land life.

CAN YOU SHOW THE BABY SEA TURTLE THE WAY FROM THE SAND TO THE WATER?

START

Baby green sea turtles have a special egg tooth that they use to break their shell and hatch out of their eggs.

Unlike other geese, the Hawaiian goose's feet are not completely webbed. It has longer toes and padded feet to walk on rocky terrain.

The Hawaiian Islands
are 3,200 km (2000 mi)
away from the nearest
land—that's about as
far as 380,000 buses
placed end to end.

FINISH

The endangered
Hawaiian monk seal
is the rarest seal in
American waters.

43

OUT AT SEA

Out in the open ocean, huge creatures swim, spin, and bask in the sun.

The enormous ocean sunfish, or mola mola, is born with a back fin that never grows.

START

GUIDE THE BOAT ACROSS THE WATER TO THE POD OF DOLPHINS.

44

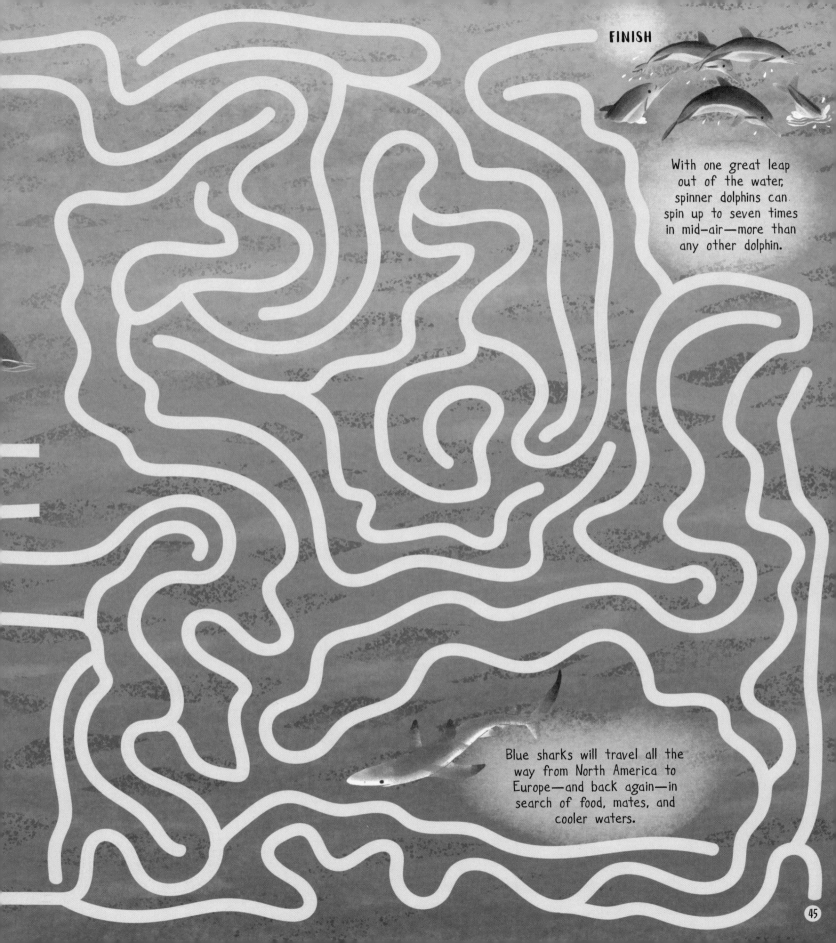

FINISH

With one great leap out of the water, spinner dolphins can spin up to seven times in mid-air—more than any other dolphin.

Blue sharks will travel all the way from North America to Europe—and back again—in search of food, mates, and cooler waters.

45

DEEP-SEA DWELLERS

Down at the bottom of the ocean, strange creatures have adapted to extremely cold waters and zero sunlight.

The Dumbo octopus propels itself through the water by flapping its large, ear–like fins and steering with its webbed arms.

More people have been to the Moon than have gone to the deepest part of the ocean.

START

CAN YOU HELP THE FANGTOOTH FISH SWIM TOWARD THE SURFACE TO FIND MORE PREY?

The anglerfish uses a dangling light above its head to lure prey toward its mouth.

Blobfish look very different out of the water than they do in it, because the pressure of the deep sea holds their shape.

47

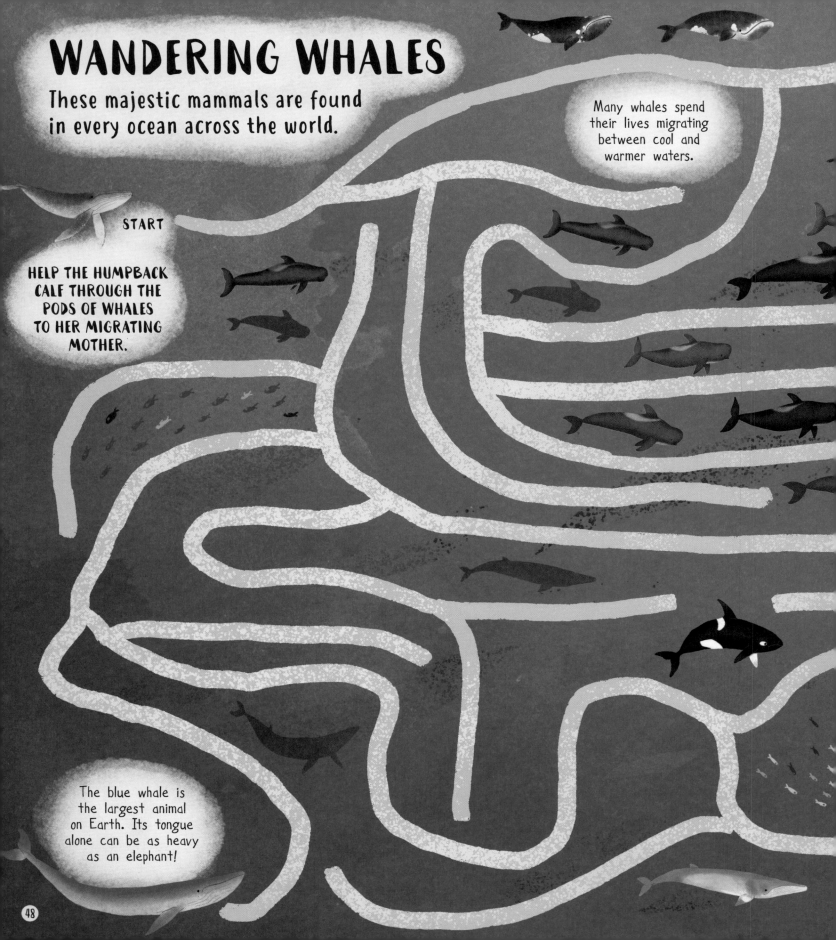

WANDERING WHALES

These majestic mammals are found in every ocean across the world.

Many whales spend their lives migrating between cool and warmer waters.

START

HELP THE HUMPBACK CALF THROUGH THE PODS OF WHALES TO HER MIGRATING MOTHER.

The blue whale is the largest animal on Earth. Its tongue alone can be as heavy as an elephant!

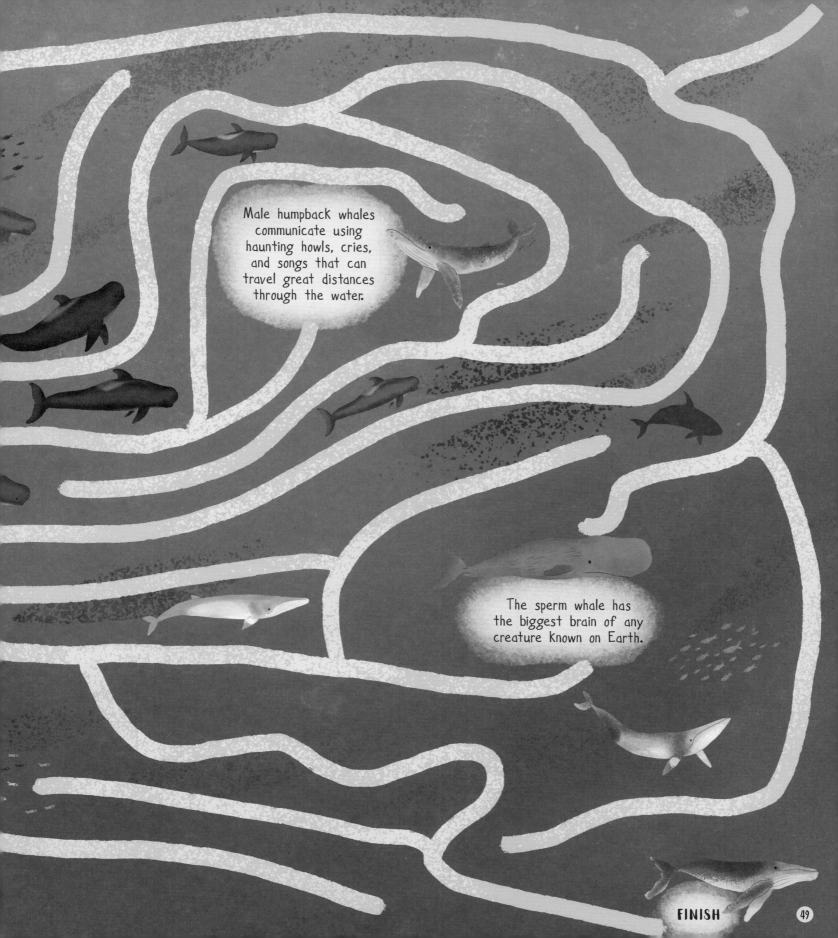

Male humpback whales communicate using haunting howls, cries, and songs that can travel great distances through the water.

The sperm whale has the biggest brain of any creature known on Earth.

TRIP AROUND THE WORLD

The Arctic tern has the longest known migration of any animal, going from the Arctic to the Antarctic and back again every year.

START

HELP THE ARCTIC TERN COMPLETE ITS WORLDWIDE JOURNEY THROUGH THE CLOUDS.

Small sand eel fish bury themselves in sand to hibernate in the winter and to hide from predators, such as birds.

The Arctic tern is so lightweight that it can float on the breeze, covering long distances without using too much energy. It can even eat while gliding!

Arctic terns don't fly straight from north to south. They wander back and forth, making their journey even longer.

FINISH

DOWN IN THE GROUND

Beneath your feet, busy animals dig, burrow, and dwell in a maze of tunnels and chambers.

SHOW THE BADGER THE WAY TO ITS BED.

START

Moles spend most of their lives alone, digging tunnels and living underground.

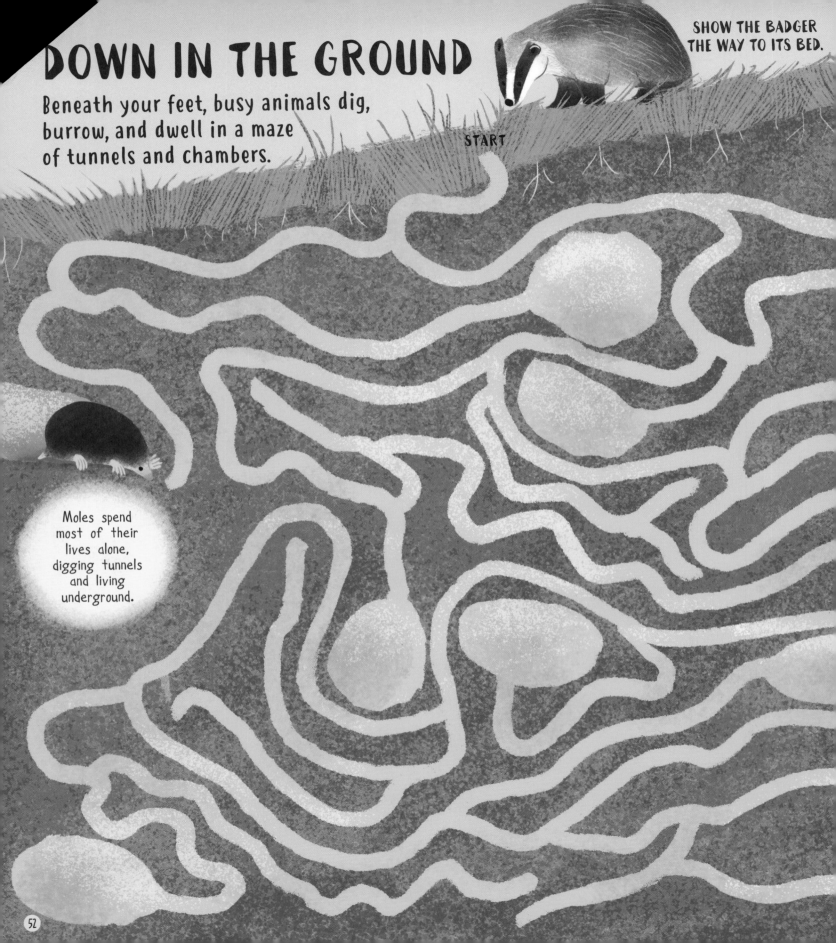

WATERY WETLANDS

In England, many animals make their homes in watery reed beds and the branches above.

Water voles eat 80% of their own body weight in food every single day.

LEAD THE WATER VOLE SAFELY THROUGH THE REEDS.

START

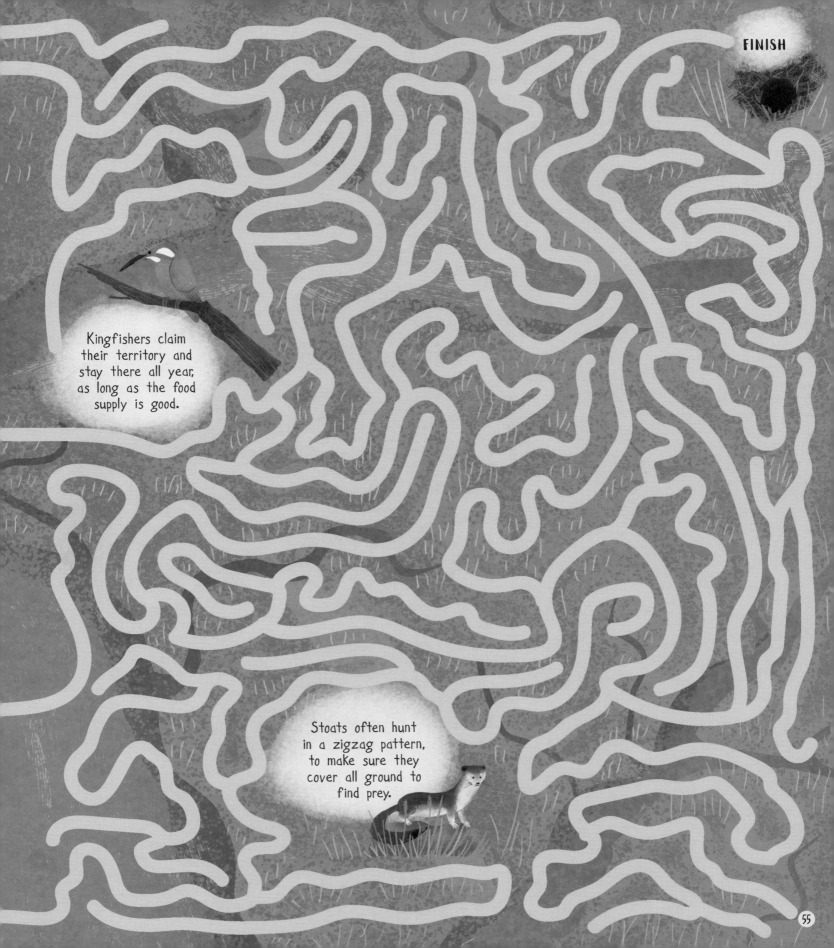

FINISH

Kingfishers claim their territory and stay there all year, as long as the food supply is good.

Stoats often hunt in a zigzag pattern, to make sure they cover all ground to find prey.

CREATURES OF THE NIGHT

After the lights go out, nocturnal animals come out to play. Who can you spot lurking in the shadows?

Despite their mouse-like faces, bats are more closely related to humans than they are to mice. They are the only mammals in the world that can truly fly!

HELP THE HEDGEHOG THROUGH THE HEDGE TO FIND ITS NEXT MEAL IN THE PILE OF LEAVES.

START

Not actually a worm at all, the light-up glowworm is in fact a beetle.

Hedgehogs sleep curled up in prickly balls during the day and come out at night to find food.

FINISH

UP IN THE ALPS

In the high, mountainous Alps of Europe, animals live on steep slopes and climb rocky cliffs.

Not only is the Alpine ibex an excellent rock climber, it can also jump up to 1.8 m (6 ft) across crevices—without a running start.

Chamois grow thick winter coats to keep warm. Padded hooves help them grip the slippery slopes.

START

GUIDE THE EXPLORER UP THE ROCK FACE TO SEE THE VIEW.

FINISH

The Alps were
formed about
44 million years ago.

Sociable Alpine marmots
greet each other by
touching noses, and groom
each other's fur.

59

BUTTERFLY GARDEN

In some special butterfly gardens, hundreds of species of beautiful butterflies flutter around the flowers.

SHOW THE VISITOR THE WAY THROUGH THE BUTTERFLY TRAIL.

START

The common bluebottle butterfly has the most advanced eyes of any butterfly, designed to help it spot fast-moving objects as it whizzes by.

Most butterflies taste with their feet.

Tailed jays have bright green wings to help them camouflage among the leaves.

When the Indian leafwing butterfly's wings are closed, it looks like a dead leaf. But when they open, beautiful patterns are revealed!

FINISH

61

HIGH IN THE HIMALAYAS

Stretching across Asia, habitats in the Himalayas range from tropical at mountain bases to cold and snowy at soaring peaks.

It can leap distances six times its own body length, but the solitary snow leopard cannot roar.

START

HELP THE EXPLORER REACH THE SUMMIT.

LURKING IN LOWLANDS

Peer through the trees and peep through the leaves to spot incredible faces in the forests of India.

LEAD THE EXPLORER THROUGH THE TREES TO THE ELEPHANTS AT THE WATERHOLE.

START

The sun bear is the smallest member of the bear family.

The most common tiger, Bengal tigers make up half of all tigers in the wild.

The shaggy sloth bear has long, curved claws to dig ants and termites out of mounds of dirt.

The Indian elephant can produce up to 100 kg (220 lbs) of dung in just one day—that's heavier than a kangaroo!

FINISH

SLITHERING SNAKES

Watch your step! In Africa's forests and rocky savannas, snakes slither on the ground and coil coyly around trees.

Eastern green mambas spend most of their lives in trees.

START

HELP THE EXPLORER SAFELY THROUGH THE FOREST.

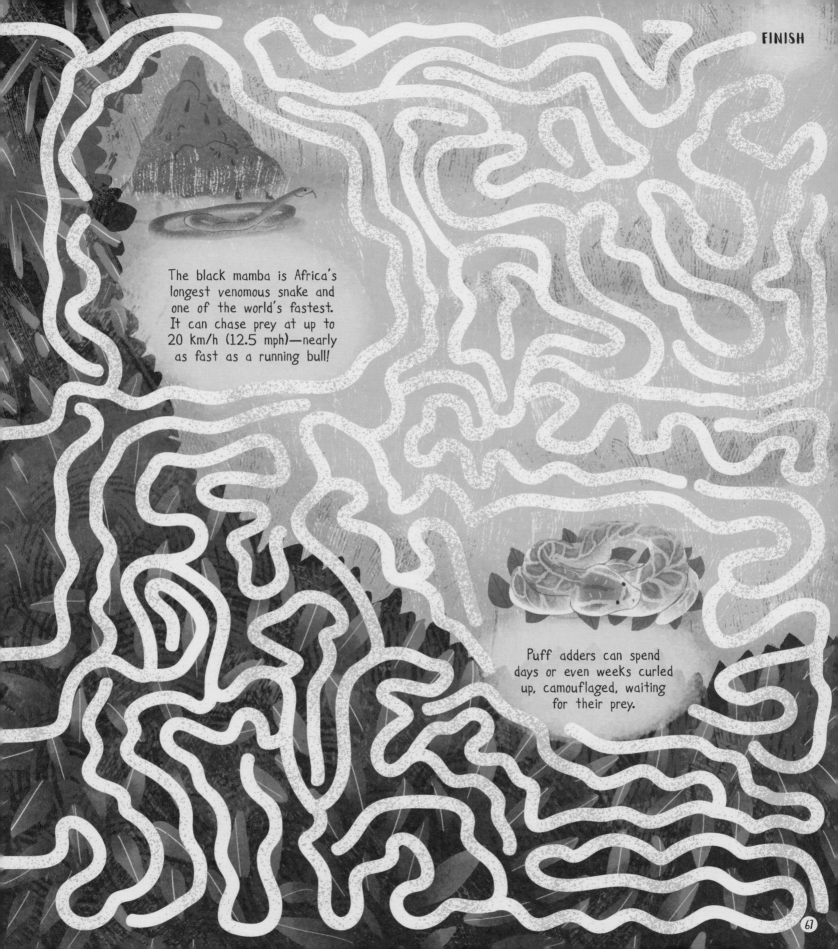

The black mamba is Africa's longest venomous snake and one of the world's fastest. It can chase prey at up to 20 km/h (12.5 mph)—nearly as fast as a running bull!

Puff adders can spend days or even weeks curled up, camouflaged, waiting for their prey.

LAKES AND LAGOONS

Paddling in shallow lagoons, magnificent mammals and beautiful birds cool down and search for their next meal.

The East African Great Lakes hold over a quarter of the world's fresh water.

HELP THE BOAT THROUGH THE FLAMBOYANCE OF FLAMINGOES.

START

Flamingoes use their webbed feet to "run" on water and work up speed to take off in flight.

The great white pelican uses its long, pouched beak to scoop up water and fish.

FINISH

Hippos spend their days in the water, staying cool in the African sun.

SUNNY SAVANNA

For half the year, tropical grasslands are bathed in hot, dry sun. The other half of the year is rainy, and the grass grows tall, perfect for grazing animals.

GUIDE THE EXPLORERS THROUGH THEIR AFRICAN SAFARI.

START

The fastest animals on land, cheetahs can go from 0 to 97 km/h (60 mph) in three seconds—faster than most cars.

The pangolin is covered in scales made of keratin—the same material as your fingernails.

Each zebra's pattern of stripes is unique, just like a human's fingerprints.

Giraffes are the tallest land mammals on the planet. Their legs alone are taller than most humans!

FINISH

71

UNDER COVER OF NIGHT

Lit only by the stars, the African bush teems with animal activity in the deep, dark night.

HELP THE BUSH BABY THROUGH THE DARKNESS TO ITS FAMILY IN THE TREES.

START

The bush baby, or galago, has huge eyes and large ears to help it see and hear in the dark.

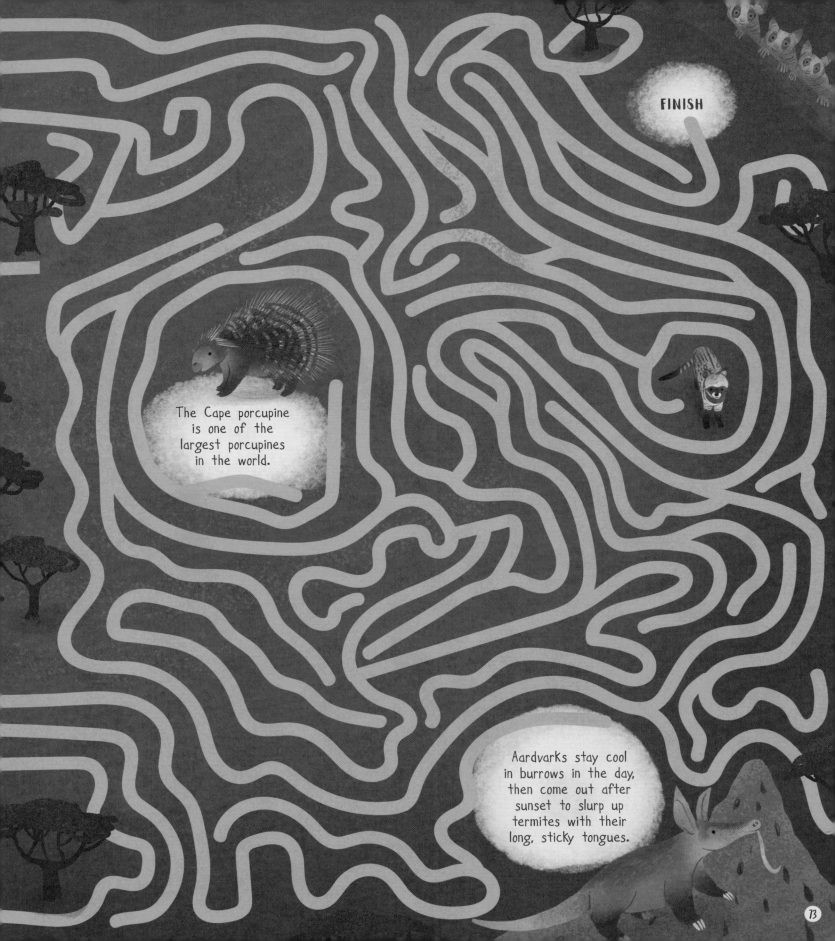

FINISH

The Cape porcupine is one of the largest porcupines in the world.

Aardvarks stay cool in burrows in the day, then come out after sunset to slurp up termites with their long, sticky tongues.

SANDY SAHARA

In the largest hot desert in the world, animals have adapted to scorching heat and very little water.

START

HELP THE EXPLORERS TO THE NEXT OASIS OF WATER.

The great Sahara Desert covers most of northern Africa—an area nearly as big as the United States.

Addax use their large, broad hooves like snowshoes to avoid sinking in the sand.

The dromedary camel stores fat in its hump so that it can go for days or even months without eating or drinking.

To keep cool, fennec foxes have large ears to let out heat, thick hair to protect them from the sun, and fur on their feet to protect them from blistering sand.

FINISH

ALONG THE NILE

The mighty Nile River is an important source of life to mammals, reptiles, fish, and birds.

The Nile is one of the longest rivers in the world. It flows through 11 countries!

HELP THE BOAT CROSS THE NILE.

START

The fearsome Nile crocodile is Africa's largest crocodilian. It can grow up to 6 m (20 ft) long and weigh as much as a grand piano!

FINISH

Along with the usual gills to breathe in water, the African lungfish has lungs to breathe in air.

With a soft, fleshy, leathery shell, the African softshell turtle can move easily in open water.

77

SPIDERS AND SILK

There are over 45,000 known species of spiders across the world, all spinning silk and going about their lives in their own way.

The golden orb-weaving spider's webs are so huge and strong that they can trap small birds.

START

HELP THE BEETLE
SAFELY THROUGH
THE GOLDEN
SPIDER WEBS.

Ogre-faced spiders spin their webs into nets that they can throw over unsuspecting prey.

A relative of the tarantula, the large, hairy baboon spider eats insects, small rodents, and even small reptiles if it can manage it.

MURKY MANGROVES

With their tropical trees growing in salty water, the mangroves of Borneo are a unique home to many well-adapted creatures.

GUIDE THE BOAT THROUGH THE TREES TO STABLE SHORE.

START

The proboscis monkey lives in the trees but loves to swim. It dives down from the branches and lands on the water with a flop!

The fiddler crab is named after its enlarged claw, which it holds like a fiddle.

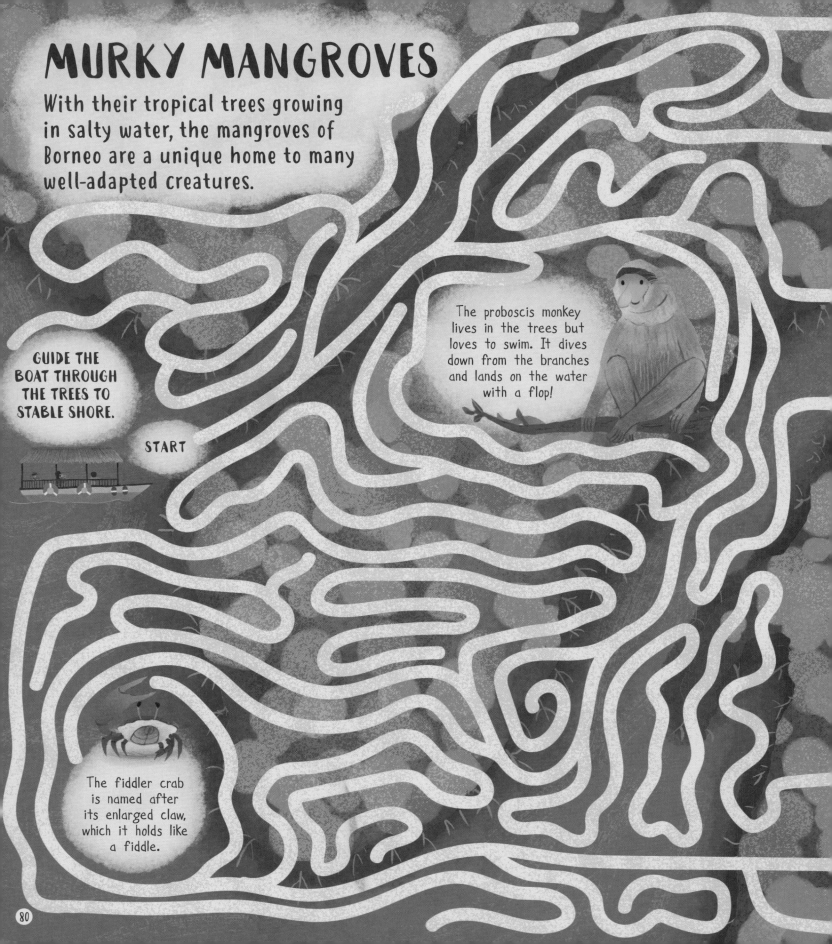

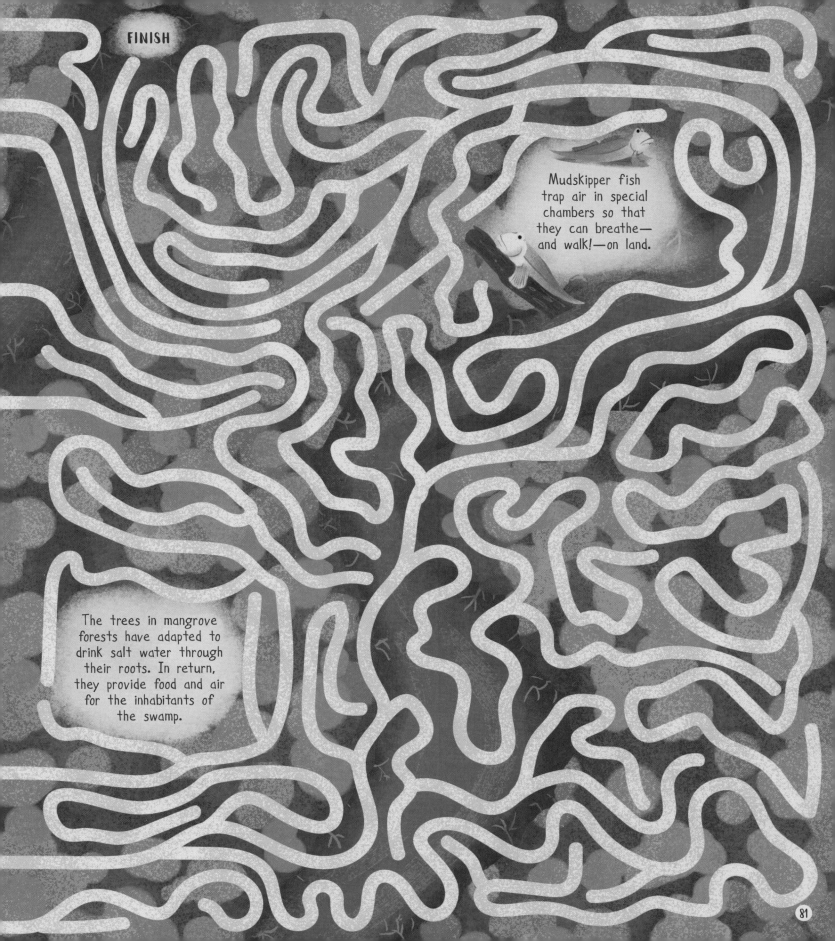

IN THE CORAL REEF

Bright coral reefs are not only incredibly beautiful to look at, they also provide homes and shelter to thousands of living species.

START

LEAD THE CLOWNFISH TO ITS ANEMONE.

After using their parrot-like beaks to scrape and nibble coral and algae, parrotfish poop out new sand for the reef!

Each coral is a living animal called a polyp. They have hard outer skeletons and are stuck in one place their whole life.

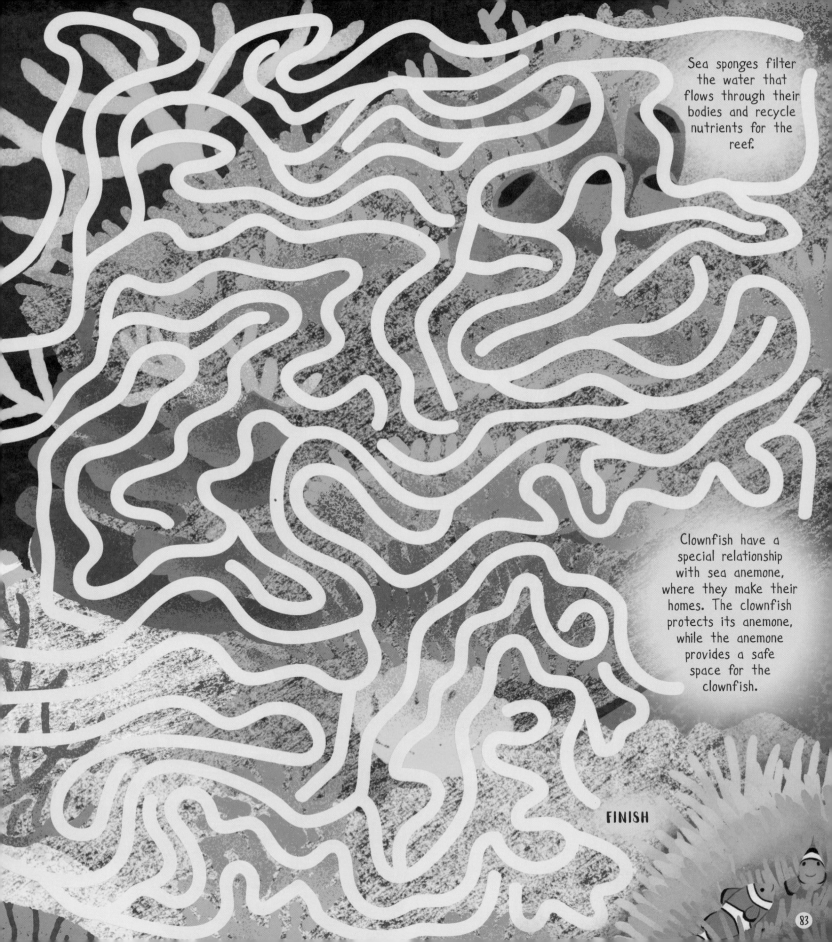

Sea sponges filter the water that flows through their bodies and recycle nutrients for the reef.

Clownfish have a special relationship with sea anemone, where they make their homes. The clownfish protects its anemone, while the anemone provides a safe space for the clownfish.

FINISH

ACROSS AUSTRALIA

The largest island in the area of Oceania, Australia is home to some famous furry faces.

HELP THE EXPLORER FIND THE WAY TO HER YURT.

START

Koalas have two thumbs on each front foot, plus a thumb on each back foot. These help them climb and cling to trees.

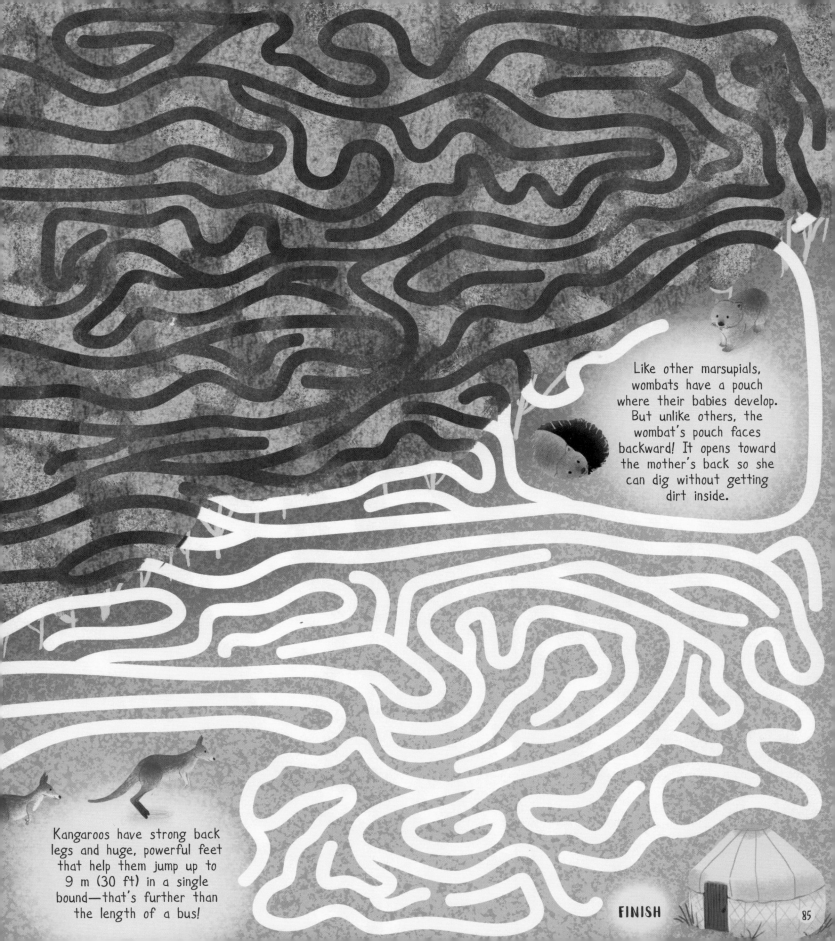

Like other marsupials, wombats have a pouch where their babies develop. But unlike others, the wombat's pouch faces backward! It opens toward the mother's back so she can dig without getting dirt inside.

Kangaroos have strong back legs and huge, powerful feet that help them jump up to 9 m (30 ft) in a single bound—that's further than the length of a bus!

FINISH

OUT IN THE OUTBACK

In the middle of Australia is a vast, dry, hot place without many people at all. Some wild animals, however, make their homes here.

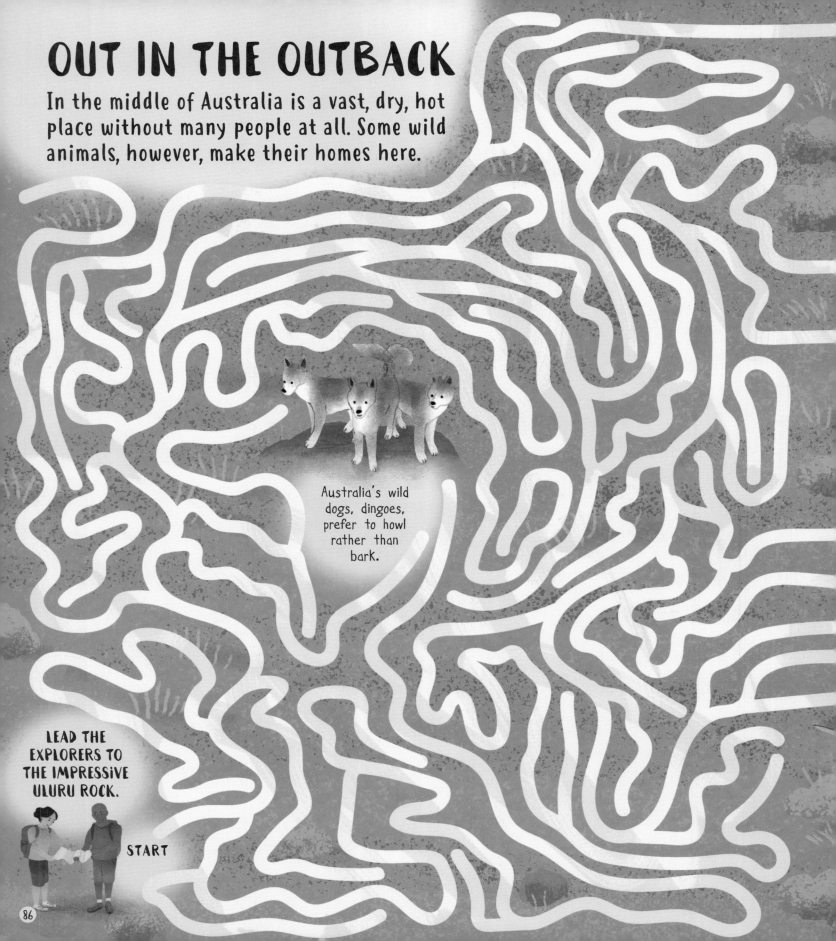

Australia's wild dogs, dingoes, prefer to howl rather than bark.

LEAD THE EXPLORERS TO THE IMPRESSIVE ULURU ROCK.

START

FINISH

The frilled lizard intimidates prey with a hiss of its large mouth and a flash of its bright neck frill.

Sand goannas can run short distances on their hind legs. They will also stand on their back legs to scare off attackers or look for danger.

CREEPY-CRAWLY CREATURES

Keep your eyes peeled as you creep through the leaves... there might just be some bugs crawling around too!

START

SHOW THE ULYSSES BUTTERFLY THE WAY THROUGH THE LEAVES.

Even though its wings are bright and eye-catching, the jewel beetle likely uses them for camouflage—they confuse predators by shimmering in the sunshine and blending in among the leaves.

The female giant prickly stick insect has thorny spikes to defend itself and hide in the trees.

One of the world's largest moths, the Hercules moth rarely eats! It has no mouth and survives off food that it stored when it was a caterpillar.

FINISH

IN ICY SEAS

Amid floating ice and chilly waves, incredible animals both big and small thrive in frigid waters.

HELP THE RESEARCHERS THROUGH THE PACK ICE TO LAND.

START

Southern elephant seals are the planet's largest seals. Males can be up to 6 m (20 ft) long— that's as long as a giraffe is high!

Food to hundreds of Antarctic species, krill like to stay in huge groups. Their swarms can sometimes be so big that they can be seen from space!

Killer whales, or orcas, are not whales at all, but the world's largest dolphin.

91

AT THE BOTTOM OF THE WORLD

On a continent covered mostly by ice, animals have unique ways of living in this cold, harsh environment.

HELP THE MOTHER PENGUIN THROUGH THE HUDDLE TO HER EGG.

START

The cold, icy landscape of Antarctica is in fact a desert, because it gets so little water from the sky.

The Antarctic petrel can produce a solution that helps its body remove the extra salt it takes in from diving for fish in salty waters.

FINISH

Male emperor penguins balance eggs on their feet to keep them warm until they hatch, while females leave for months to find food.

93

ANSWERS

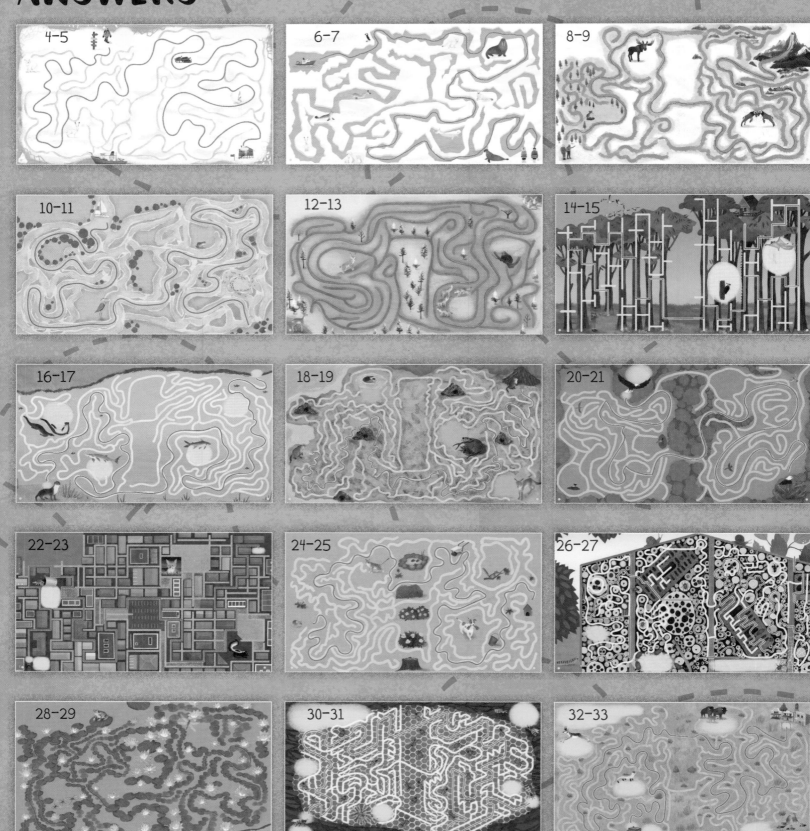

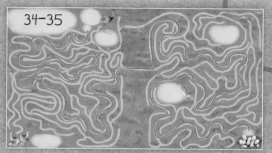

34-35

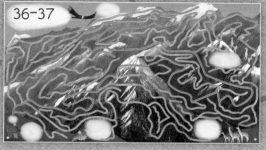

36-37

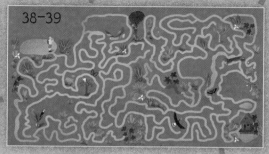

38-39

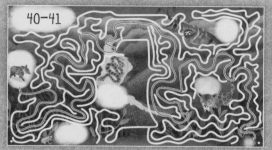

40-41

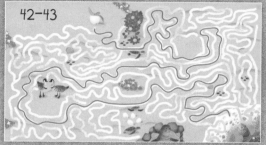

42-43

44-45

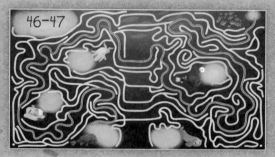

46-47

48-49

50-51

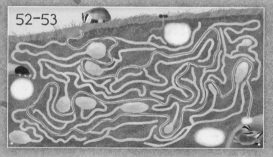

52-53

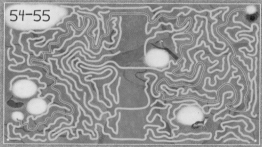

54-55

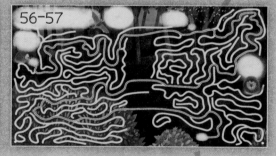

56-57

58-59

60-61

62-63

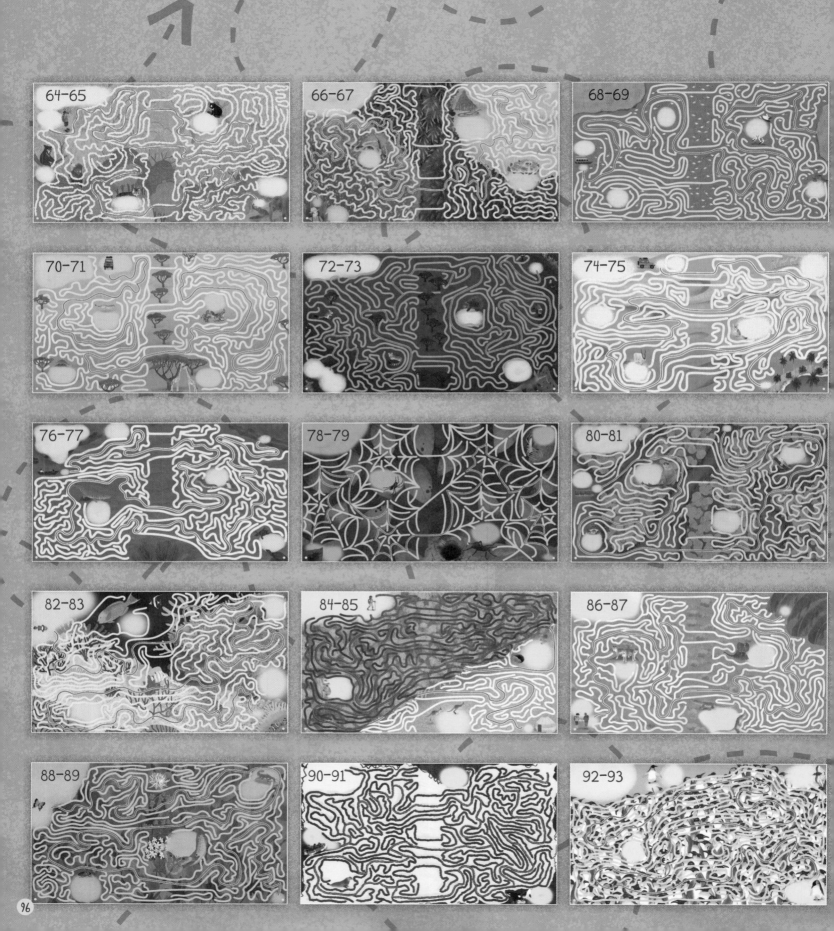